Year 4
Workbook

Pearson

Published by Pearson Education Limited, 80 Strand, London, WC2R 0RL.

www.pearson.com/international-schools

Copies of official specifications for all Pearson Edexcel qualifications may be found on the website: https://qualifications.pearson.com

Text © Pearson Education Limited 2023
Produced by Just Content Ltd
Designed by PDQ Media Digital Media Solutions
Typeset by PDQ Media Digital Media Solutions
Picture research by Straive Ltd
Original illustrations © Pearson Education Limited 2023
Cover design © Pearson Education Limited 2023

The right of Lesley Butcher to be identified as the author of this work has been asserted by her in accordance with the Copyright, Designs and Patents Act 1988.

First published 2023

26 25 24
10 9 8

British Library Cataloguing in Publication Data
A catalogue record for this book is available from the British Library

ISBN 978 1 292 43326 4

Printed in UK by Bell & Bain

Contents

1 Variation and classification 2

2 Growing plants 18

3 Skeleton and muscles 50

4 Solids, liquids and gases 70

5 Making and changing sounds 94

6 Electricity: everyday uses and simple circuits ... 122

Variation and classification

Scientists classify living things by looking at features they share. Vertebrates and invertebrates are two big groups of animals. Within these two groups, some animals have many legs, but others have fewer. Scientists can classify plants by looking at features such as their leaves or flowers.

In this topic we will learn:

- how living things can be classified according to shared features

- to explore and use classification keys to help group, identify and name living things

- to describe how plants and animals are classified

- how to identify the observable features used to classify a specific plant or animal.

My features differ from Asha and Marco because I am not human. Can you see three ways in which I differ from a human?

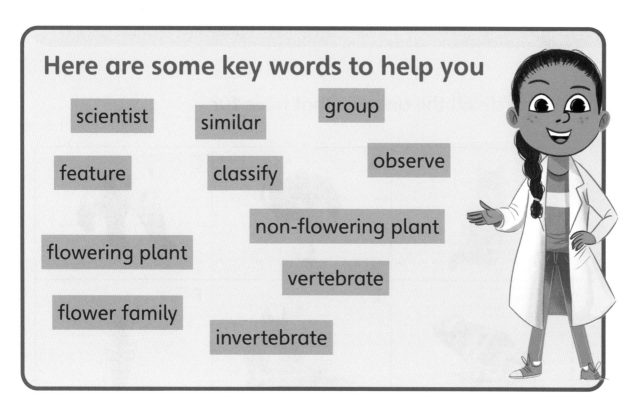

Here are some key words to help you

scientist

similar

group

feature

classify

observe

non-flowering plant

flowering plant

vertebrate

flower family

invertebrate

Choose two key words from the box above.
Write or draw what they mean.

Shared features

1 a)   Circle all the animals that have **fur**.

b)   Which letter shows an animal with **six** legs? _____

c)   Write all the letters of animals that are **vertebrates**.

_____

2 a)   Write **two** features that these animals all share.

1. _____   2. _____

b) Write **two** features that these animals all share.

1. _____

2. _____

3 This bat is a **mammal**.   This butterfly is an **insect**.

Suggest **two** reasons why they are **not** grouped together.

1. _____

    _____

2. _____

    _____

Identifying local plants

1 What is the scientific word for the place where a plant is found? _____

2 Look at some of the plants that grow where you live.

    a)   Draw the shape of two different trees you can see. Name them if you can.

> Draw with solid lines like this:
>
> Not fuzzy lines like this:

    b)   Label the **trunk** and the **leaves**.

3 Name **two** other plants you can see.

1. _____   2. _____

4 Draw some of the plants you can see. Name them if you can.

Label a **leaf** on each one. Label a **flower** if there are any.

Classifying plants

1 a) Circle **one** word that means *put living things into groups*.

colour   measure   check   classify   test

b) (i) Circle **two** shapes that are the *same*.

(ii) Circle **two** shapes that are *similar*.

2 Draw a label line and write **F** to label a flower in each picture.

3 a) Complete this diagram by doing these things.

- Write words in boxes 1 and 2.

- Draw the missing leaf in box 3.

- Name the two plants in boxes 4 and 5.

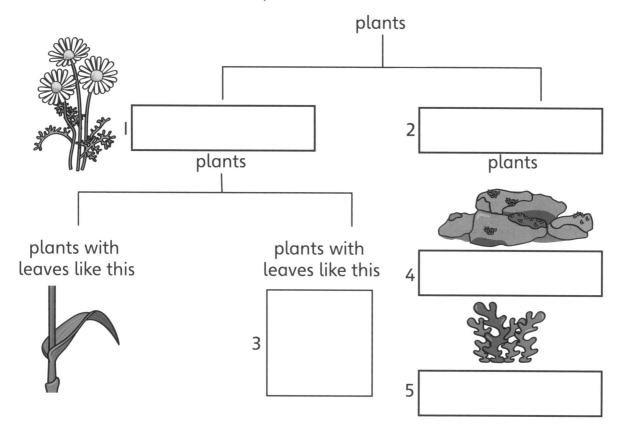

plants

1 [　　　　　　　　　]   plants

2 [　　　　　　　　　]   plants

plants

plants with leaves like this

plants with leaves like this

3 [　　　]

4 [　　　　　　　　]

5 [　　　　　　　　]

b) Name **two** flowering plants.

1. _____   2. _____

4 Circle the plants with similar leaves.

Classifying animals

1 a) Circle **two** groups that an **owl** is classified into.

mammal   bird   vertebrate   invertebrate

b) (i) A cheetah and a snow leopard are both grouped in the cat family.

Write **two** features they share.

1. _____   2. _____

(ii) Write **two** other groups they are classified in.

1. _____   2. _____

2 Write the names of vertebrate groups **A**, **B**, **C** and **D**.

animals

vertebrates   invertebrates

(animals with backbones)   (animals without backbones)

A   B   C   D   mammals

A	
C	

B	
D	

3 Write information **from the key** for all your answers in question 3.

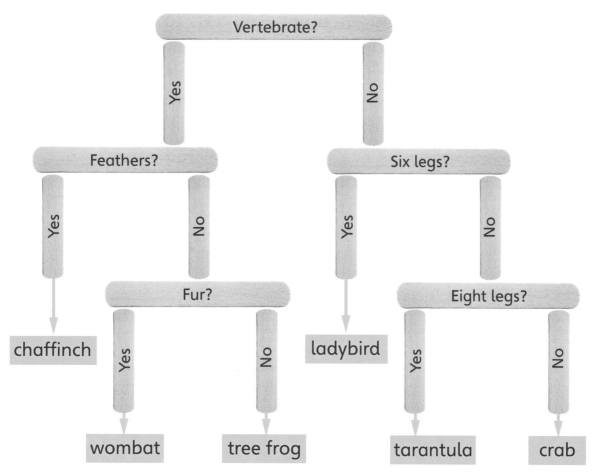

a) Which animal in the key has **feathers**? _____

b) Which animal has eight legs? _____

c) Write **two** features to describe a **ladybird**.

    I. _____   2. _____

d) Write **two** features to describe a **wombat**.

    I. _____   2. _____

Observing a plant

1 **a)** Carefully join the numbered dots to draw this buttercup flower. Then colour it in.

b) Label **flower**, **petal**, **leaf** and **stem** using a label line and the word each time.

c) How many petals does each flower have?

2 These flowers are in the same flower family.

buttercup   **flower A**   **flower B**

a)   Write **two** different words to describe the buttercup flower. Start with its colour.

1. _____   2. _____

b)   Describe this buttercup leaf.
     Start with its colour.

_____

_____

c)   Write **one** feature both **flower A** and the buttercup share.

_____

d)   **Flower B** is also in the same flower family as a buttercup.

     Write **one** feature they share and **one** way they differ.

share   _____

differ   _____

Observing an animal

1 a) Label the earthworm by naming the parts shown.

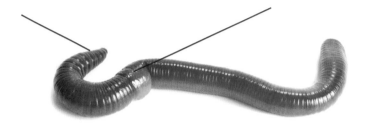

b) Add your own label to show **segments**.

c) Where do earthworms live?

_____

d) Why do earthworms need to sense light and dark?

_____

2 Describe how an earthworm moves.

_____

_____

3 What sort of animals are predators of earthworms?

_____

4 Find out and write **two** examples of what earthworms eat.

1. _____

2. _____

5 This is a leech. It is grouped with earthworms.

Look at its body features.

Write **two** features it shares with the earthworm in question 1.

1. _____

2. _____

6 This is a centipede.
It is **not** grouped with earthworms.

Look at its features.

Suggest **one** reason it is **not** grouped with earthworms.

_____

_____

What have I learned?

1 I can explain how living things can be classified according to shared features.

I know this because I can write **three** features that these two animals share.

1. _____

2. _____

3. _____

2 I can explore and use classification keys to help me group, identify and name a variety of living things.

I know this because I can write a question that will be:

yes for animal **A**   and   **no** for animal **B**.

A    B

My question is: _____

_____

3 I can describe how plants and animals are classified by observing features that are similar and features that differ.

I know this because I can write **one** feature of these plants that is **similar** and **one** way they **differ**.

similar _____

different _____

4 I can identify the observable features used to classify a specific plant such as a buttercup.

I know this because I can draw lines to label:

yellow petal

leaf

serrated edge

5 I can identify the observable features used to classify a specific animal such as an earthworm.

I know this because I can draw and label an earthworm.

earthworm	

Growing plants

Plants differ in many ways, but they all need certain things to grow well. We can group plants in many ways just by looking at their leaves or flowers. Plants are living things so they need water to stay alive.

In this topic we will learn:

- how to identify and describe the functions of different parts of flowering plants

- how to use a simple key with yes/no answers to identify a variety of plants

- how to group plants using features we can observe

- how water is transported within plants

- that plants need the correct amount of water and light to grow well

- that soil provides minerals to help plants grow.

Plants make their own food using their green leaves but I cannot reach the leaves of a tree. Can you think of an animal that can eat leaves from a tree?

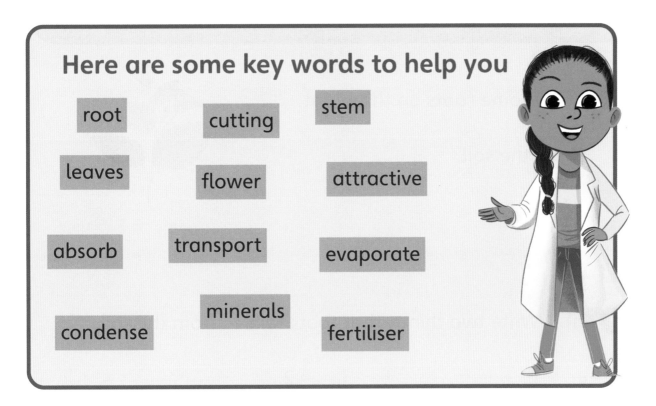

Here are some key words to help you

root

cutting

stem

leaves

flower

attractive

absorb

transport

evaporate

minerals

condense

fertiliser

Choose two key words from the box above.
Write or draw what they mean.

Roots

1 Draw some **roots** on this plant.

Draw the **soil**.

2 a) Write **two** things that roots take in from the soil.

1. _____   2. _____

b) Write **one** other job of roots.

_____

3 Write **one** scientific word to use instead of *job*.

_____

4 Why do plants need minerals?

_____

5 Look at some plants that grow where you live.

Draw with solid lines like this: _____

Not fuzzy lines like this:

Draw their roots if you can.

Name each plant.

Name: _____

Name: _____

Name: _____

Stems and trunks

1 a) Complete the **three** labels on this plant.

b) Which **three** parts of this plant does the stem hold above the ground?

1. _____   2. _____

3. _____

c) Write **one** other function of a plant's stem.

_____

2 This small plant will grow into a tree.

Describe how its stem will change as it grows.

_____

_____

_____

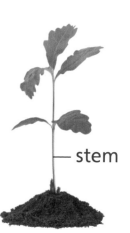

stem

3 a) Draw **two** plants that grow where you live.
Choose **one tree** and **one plant** that is **not a tree**.

b) Write as much as you can to compare your plants.
Here are some ideas:

height?	texture of stem or trunk?	woody?

_____

_____

_____

_____

Leaves

1 a) Complete the **five** labels on this plant.

b) Write a **title**.

Title: _____

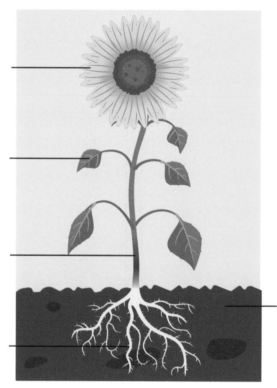

2 a) Write the scientific name for:

(i) living things that make their own food.

_____

(ii) animals that only eat plants.

_____

b) Which part of a plant makes its food?

_____

c)   Write **three** things that plants
     need to make their food.
     Look at the diagram for help.

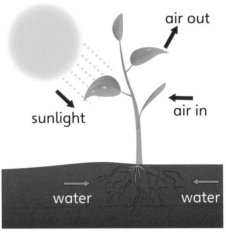

1. _____

2. _____

3. _____

3 a)   Complete the **two** labels on
        this leaf.

b)   Complete the sentences
     about leaves.

The colour of most leaves is _____.

Leaves are thin and _____ so air can go in

and _____ of them.

A wide, flat leaf can _____ a lot of sunlight.

A leaf that is facing the _____ has more light

shining on it.

Flowers

1 a)   **Name** this plant.

_____

b)   On this plant, label:
   - the stem
   - a leaf
   - a flower.

2   On this plant, label:
   - a leaf
   - a flower
   - a flower bud.

3 a)   These flowers are on a tree.
Label:
   - a petal
   - a flower bud.

b)   What can you see that shows these flowers are on a tree?

_____

4 a) Write about what flowers look like and their function.

Use this picture to help.

_____

_____

_____

b) Draw **two** different flowers.
Draw a different insect on each one.

Flower key

1 **a)** Write 'yes' or 'no' for each question in the table.

| Flower | Questions | | |
	Five petals?	White petals?	Yellow in the centre?
A 			
B 			
C 			
D 			

b) Use your answers in the table to describe **flower D**.

_____

_____

c)   Which flowers are yellow in the centre?

_____

d)   Use the information in the table to complete the key below.

(i)   Write two questions.

(ii) Write the letters of the four flowers in the correct answer boxes.

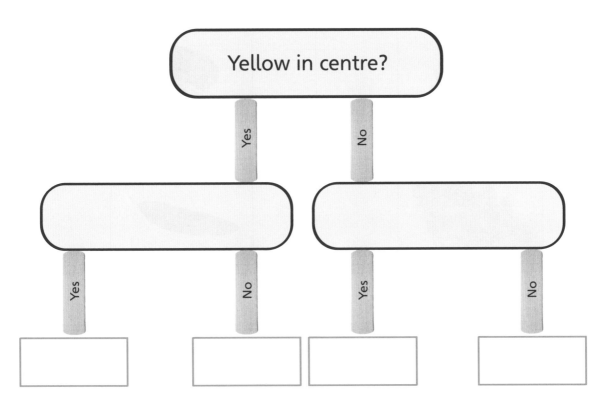

Grouping leaves

1 The drawings show some leaf shapes.

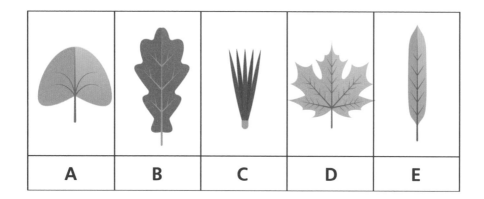

| A | B | C | D | E |

a) Write **one** letter in each box below to show the leaf shape that the picture matches best.

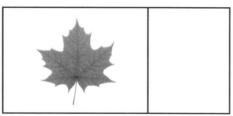

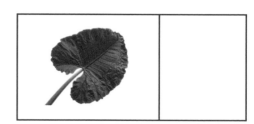

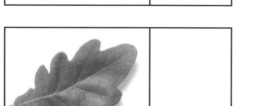

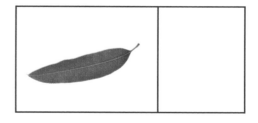

b) Draw **two** leaf shapes that you can see where you live.

2 Draw **one** line from each leaf to the one with similar **edges.**

3 Draw **two** more leaves on **each** picture.
Work out their pattern first.

Grouping flowers

1. Draw **one** line from each flower to the pattern its flowers grow in.

Flower   Pattern

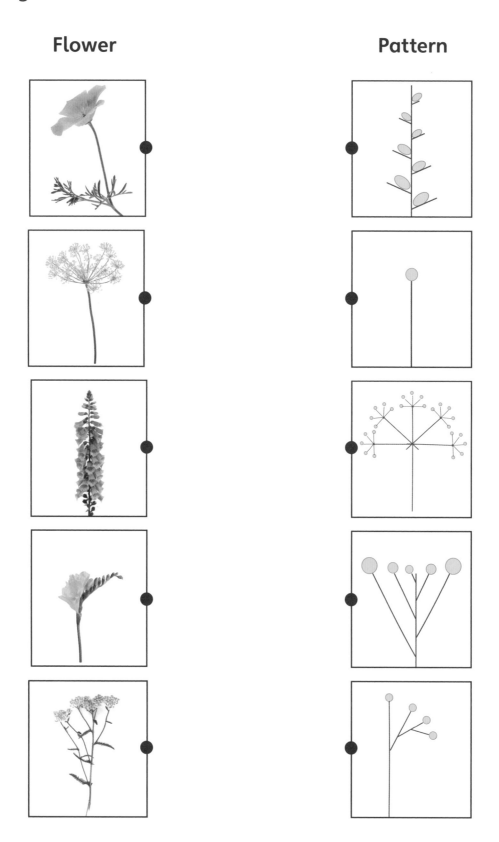

2 Draw a big flower container with flowers of different shapes. Draw flowers that grow in different patterns. Colour them. Here are some ideas.

1 a) Complete the labels for **four** parts of this tree.

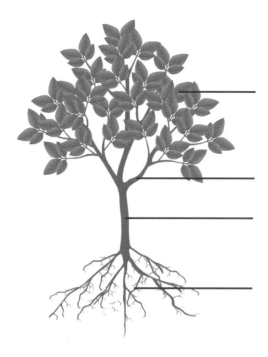

b) Write **two** functions of roots.

1. _____

2. _____

2 Class 4 put the stem of this flower into a beaker of red coloured water.

a) Finish the drawing to show this.

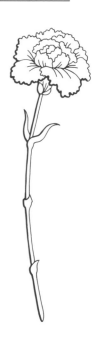

b)   The next day, the flower has changed.
     Colour this flower to show the change.

c)   Next they split the stem of another
     flower and put each part into a
     beaker of coloured water.

     Colour the flower to show how it
     looks the next day.

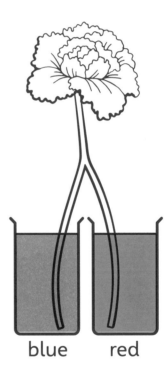

blue   red

3   Why do scientists look for **evidence**?

_____

_____

The pathway of water

1 a)   Draw **three** arrows on the plant to show:

- water entering the roots

- water moving up the stem

- water going into the leaves.

b)   Draw **two** more arrows on the plant to show:

- water evaporating from the soil into the air

- water evaporating from a leaf into the air.

2 The inside of a plant stem is full of tubes.

    a)   What moves up inside the tubes?

    _____

    b)   What happens to the tubes as the plant grows?

    _____

3 This celery is standing in some red coloured water.

    a)   Name the equipment that this water is in.

    _____

    b)   Predict what happens to the coloured water.

    _____

    c)   Colour the two pieces of celery to show what they look like the next day.

Water in leaves

1 Complete the sentences to show what is happening in the picture.

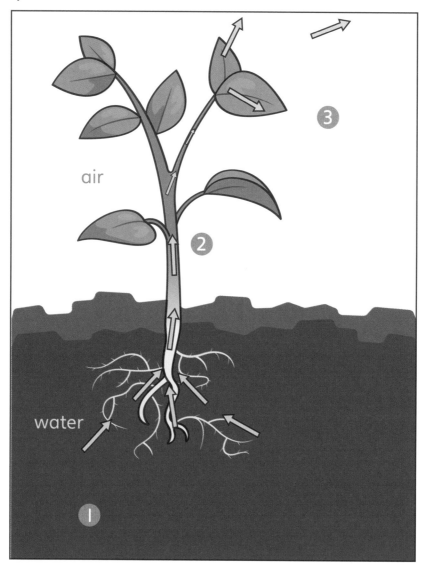

1 Roots take in _____ from the

_____.

2 Water travels up the _____ to the

_____.

3 Water _____ from the leaves.

plastic bag

2 Class 4 look for evidence that water evaporates from the leaves of a plant.

They set up this equipment.

a)   Which part of the plant is inside the pot?

_____

b)   Why do they use a **transparent** bag?

_____

c)   What do they see inside the bag the next day?

_____

d)   Can you improve their investigation to show that what they see comes from the leaves, not the soil?

Draw your answer on this plant.

Plants need water

1 These plants have not been watered.
Write **one** word under each plant to describe it.

2 Do this investigation to compare how well plants grow when given different volumes of water.

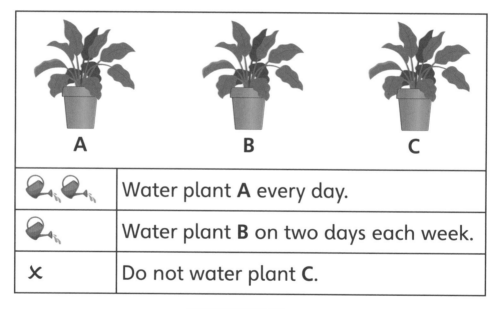

	Water plant **A** every day.	
	Water plant **B** on two days each week.	
✗	Do not water plant **C**.	

a)   What are you changing ?

_____

b)   Write **three** things you should **keep the same** for all three plants.

1. _____

2. _____

3. _____

c)   Write or draw your observations in the table.

Watering of plant	Observations		
	at start	after 1 week	after 2 weeks
A 			
B 			
C ✗			

d)   Which plant grew best?

_____

Plants need light

1 a) Write **two** different ways that plants get light.

1. _____

2. _____

b) Why do plants need light?

_____

2 Look at plants **A** and **B**.

a) Describe **one** difference in their leaves.

_____

_____

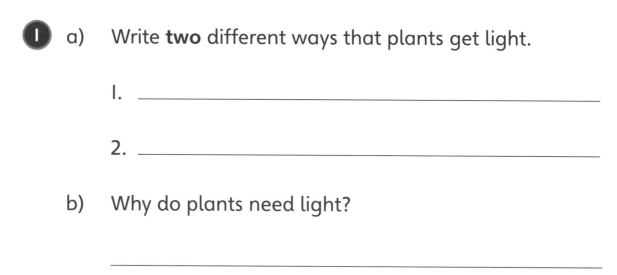

kept in a   kept in a
light place   dark place

b) Describe **one** difference in their height.

_____

3 Draw where the Sun  is in each picture below.

4 Investigate the effect of light on the growth of cress seeds.

a) Circle the factor you are [changing] .

   type of seed   temperature   light

b) What are you doing to the two factors you did **not** circle?

_____

5 a) Complete the table by drawing your seeds as they grow. Look at them from the side.

Light given to seeds	Observations	
	after I week	after 2 weeks
Light all around		
Light from one side		
No light		

b) Write a conclusion for your investigation.

_____

_____

Plants need minerals

1 Complete the sentences about minerals using words from the box. Each word may be used only **once**.

waste	nutrients	water	fruit	air
green	grow	soil	water	leaves

Minerals are extra _____ that help plants

to _____ well.

Plants take in minerals from the _____

when they take in _____.

Minerals help the plant to stay _____,

to grow new _____ and to make

_____.

2 a) Circle the part of a plant that takes in water and minerals from the soil.

　　roots　　flowers　　leaves　　petals

b) Which part of a plant do minerals go up to reach the leaves?

_____

3 The plants in the pictures at the top of the next page are not getting enough minerals.

a) Describe what has happened to each leaf.

_____   _____

_____   _____

b) (i) What is the function of leaves?

_____

(ii) Suggest what may happen to the plants in the pictures.

_____

4 a) What is this grower putting in the soil?

_____

b) Why are they doing this?

_____

c) What is this grower putting on their field?

_____

Investigating fertiliser

1 Do an investigation to answer the scientific question:

> Do plants grow taller when they are given fertiliser?

a) What will you change ? Write under the pots.

b) (i) What will you measure ? _____

(ii) What unit will you measure in? _____

c) Write **two** ways you will make this a fair test.

1. _____

2. _____

d) Why are you using **three** plants in each group?

_____

e) Why do you measure the height at the start?

_____

2 Write your results in this table.

Plant number	Plant height in cm				
	at start	after 1 week	after 2 weeks	after 3 weeks	after 4 weeks
1					
2					
3					
4					
5					
6					

a) Work out the change in height of each plant.

Plant number	Change in height in cm
1	
2	
3	
4	
5	
6	

Look at the height of plant number 1 after 4 weeks.

Subtract its height at the start.

Do that for each plant.

b) Which number plant changed height the most? ☐

c) Which number plant changed height the least? ☐

d) Do plants grow taller when they are given fertiliser?

_____

What have I learned?

1 I can identify and describe the functions of different parts of flowering plants: **roots**, **stem** or **trunk**, **leaves** and **flowers**.

I know this because I can label this plant.

2 I can use a simple key with yes/no answers to identify a variety of plants.

I know this because I can write **one** question that will be:

yes for plant **A**   and   **no** for plant **B**.

 A    B

My question is: _____

3 I can group plants using features I can observe.

I know this because I can give **one** reason why these plants are grouped together.

_____

4 I understand the way water is transported within plants.

I can describe the pathway of water as being from the soil into the plant's roots and up through the stem to the leaves and other parts of the plant.

I know this because I can **draw arrows** on this plant to show water moving from the roots to the leaves.

5 I understand that plants need the correct amount of water and light to grow well.

I know this because I can describe plants **A**, **B** and **C**.

A	B	C

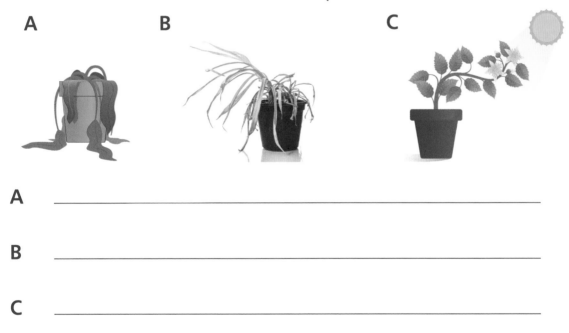

A _____

B _____

C _____

6 I understand that soil provides minerals to help plants grow, and that fertilisers and organic matter add more minerals.

I know this because I can show my teacher how I described the leaves on page 45.

Skeleton and muscles

Humans have a skeleton to support their bodies. Our skeleton also helps us to move. When muscles contract, they pull bones into different positions. Places where bones meet are called joints. Some parts of our skeleton protect important organs.

In this topic we will learn:

- that humans have internal skeletons with four functions

- to identify and locate the skull and rib cage

- that the term 'joint' describes the place where bones meet

- the terms 'contract' and 'relax'

- to describe what pairs of muscles do

- about the importance of exercise and diet for healthy muscles and bones.

Humans and other vertebrates have a skeleton inside their bodies. It is made from lots of bones.

Can you feel your bones?

Find out which part of your body contain the longest bone.

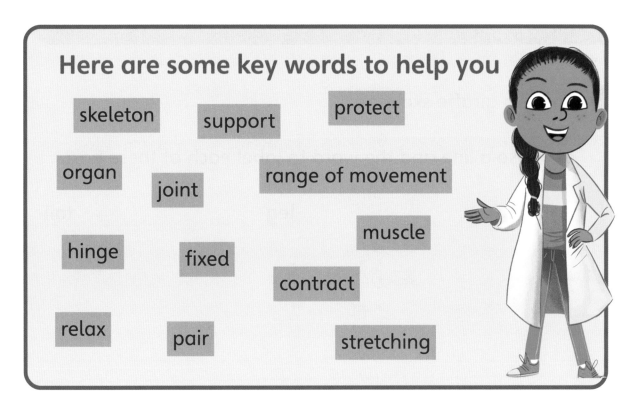

Here are some key words to help you

skeleton

support

protect

organ

joint

range of movement

hinge

muscle

fixed

contract

relax

pair

stretching

Choose two key words from the box above.
Write or draw what they mean.

The human skeleton: support

1 This is a giraffe skeleton.

a) Use a line and the word to label each of these parts.

neck   **leg**   **tail**

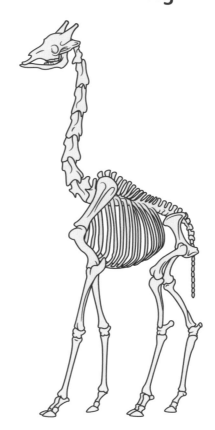

b) What are all the parts of a skeleton called? _____

c) (i) What do scientists call animals with backbones?

_____

(ii) Label the giraffe's **backbone**.

d) What do scientists call animals **without** backbones?

_____

2 This is a human skeleton.

a)   Use a line and the word to label each of these parts.

neck   **leg**   **arm**   **hand**   **foot**

b)   Why are there no ears or nose on the skeleton?

_____

c)   Write a sentence to compare the **size** of the bones in the neck of the giraffe skeleton with the bones in the human neck.

_____

_____

1   Name these organs.

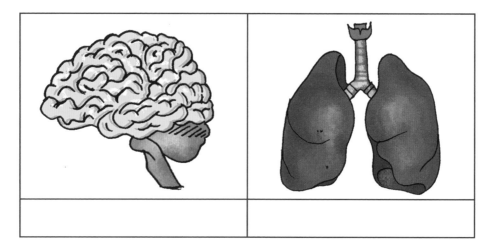

2   a)   Complete the **three** labels on this diagram.

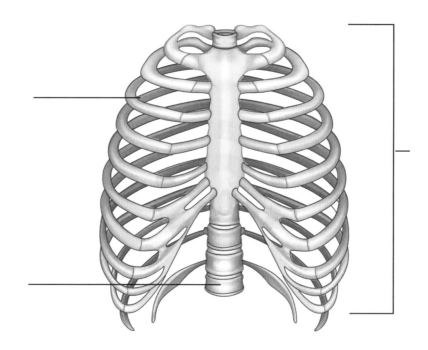

b)   Which organs do these bones protect?

_____

3 a)   Name the bone shown in the picture below.

_____

b)   What is this bone protecting?   _____

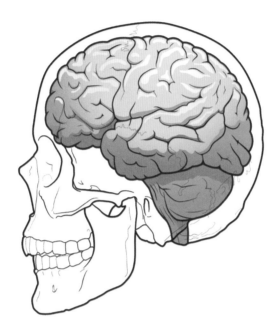

c)   Draw a line and write the bold word to label:

- something that is **hard** and

- something that is **soft** in the picture.

4   Eggs are easily damaged.

Work with a partner.

Imagine you each have an egg
to carry home.

Discuss some ways you could protect your eggs
from damage.

The human skeleton: movement

1 a) Use a line and the word to label each of these parts of the skeleton.

skull   **rib cage**   **elbow**   **knee**   **hand**

b) Describe **four** different functions of a human skeleton.

1. _____

2. _____

3. _____

4. _____

2   a)   Complete the labels to name **six** joints shown in the picture.

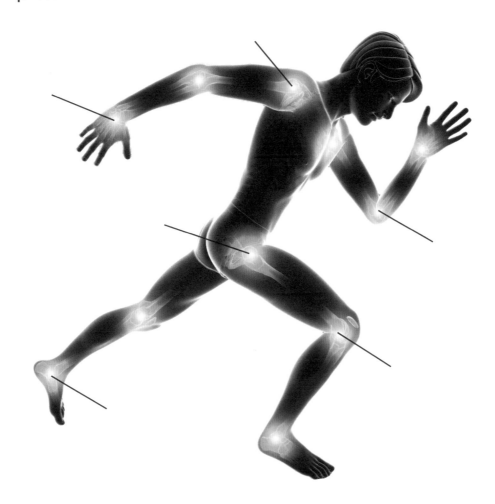

b)   Complete the sentences.

A joint is where two or more _____ meet.

Bones stay the same shape because they are

_____.

Joints allow our body to _____ position

so we can _____.

Elbows and knees

1 a) Circle the name of the joint shown in the picture.

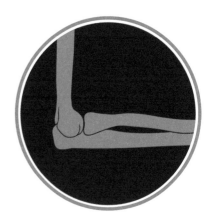

hip shoulder knee elbow

b) Circle the place where this joint is found.

rib cage   arm   leg   skull

c) How many bones meet at this joint? ⬜

2 This type of joint is a **hinge** joint.

a) Draw an arrow to show the directions in which this hinge joint moves.

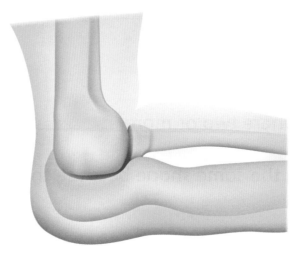

b) Name something in your classroom that has **hinges**.

_____

3 This is a knee joint. It is also a hinge joint.

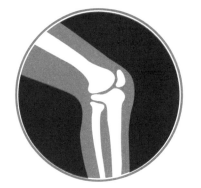

a) Draw an arrow to show the directions in which this hinge joint moves.

b) (i) Draw a label line and write **knee cap** in the correct place.

(ii) What is the function of the knee cap?

_____

(iii) How many **other** bones meet at this joint? ☐

4 This diagram shows a frog skeleton.

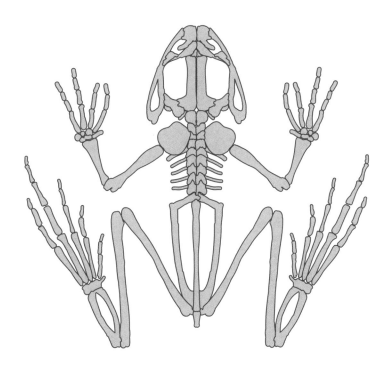

Circle **one** joint that is like a knee.

Draw **one** square around a joint that is like an elbow.

More types of joint

1 a) Circle the name of the joint shown in the picture.

hip   shoulder   knee   elbow

b) How many bones can you see in the picture of this joint?

c) Describe the directions in which this joint moves.

_____

2 a) Circle the name of the joint shown in the picture.

hip   shoulder   knee   elbow

b) Does this joint have a **bigger** or a **smaller** range of movement than a hinge joint? _____

3 The top of the skull has a fixed joint. Describe this fixed joint.

_____

_____

_____

4 The pictures show a girl moving her neck joint.

Draw **one** line from each picture to the direction the girl's neck moves in.

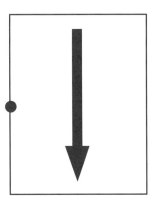

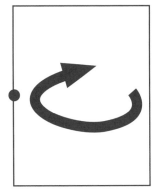

Muscles

1 a) Write the word **muscle** or **bone**

  • to complete **three** labels and

  • in the **two** spaces in the sentence.

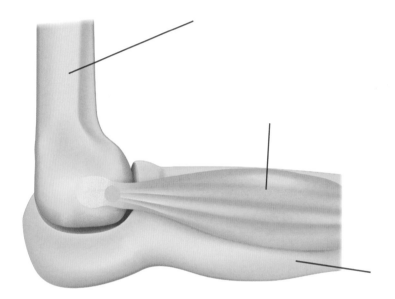

The _____ is attached to the _____ .

b) What do muscles do to bones? Circle **one** answer.

push   pull   squeeze   twist

c) Is each end of a muscle attached to the **same** bone or to **different** bones?

_____

d) Why do muscles look red in colour?

_____

2 This boy is bending his arm.

a) Draw a line and write the words to label:

- elbow joint

- biceps muscle

- wrist joint.

b) Complete the sentences using words from the box. Use each word **once**.

contracts	relaxes	fatter
thinner	shorter	longer

When a muscle contracts it gets _____

and _____.

The biceps muscle _____ to bend the arm.

To make the arm straight, the biceps muscle

_____ and goes back to its starting length.

Contracting and relaxing

1 a) Which part of the body does the diagram show?
Circle your answer.

arm   neck   leg   rib cage   skull

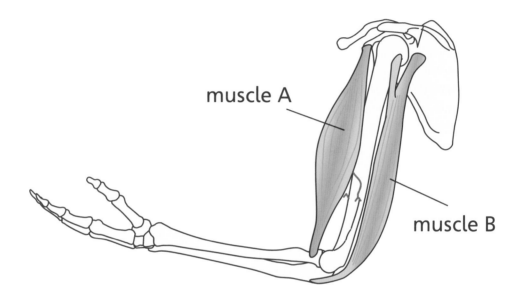

muscle A

muscle B

b) Draw a line and write the word to label **two** different parts of the diagram that show a **bone**.

c) Name muscles A and B.

Muscle A is the _____.

Muscle B is the _____.

d) When muscle A contracts, what does muscle B do?

_____

e) Muscle A and B work as a pair. What does *pair* mean?

_____

2 The diagrams show **four** muscles.

Write **contracts** or **relaxes** next to each label.

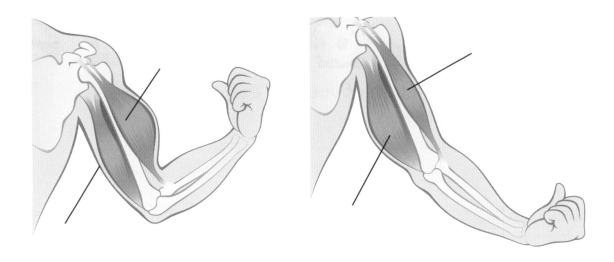

3 Bend and straighten your foot. Describe what you feel happening at the front and back of your lower leg.

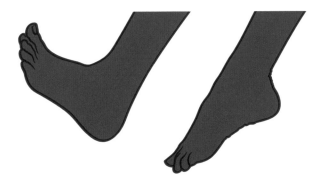

_____

_____

_____

Healthy muscles and bones

1. These children are exercising.

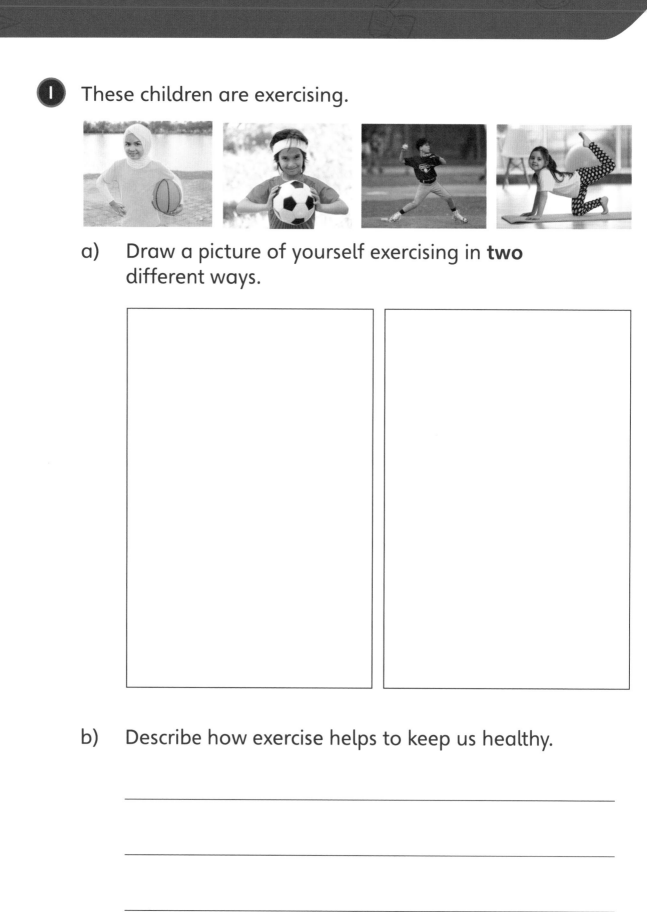

   a) Draw a picture of yourself exercising in **two** different ways.

   b) Describe how exercise helps to keep us healthy.

   _____

   _____

   _____

2 Dairy foods help to build growing bones.
Other foods help too.

a) Draw food that you like to eat that is
good for growing bones.

**food for
growing
bones**

b) Protein foods help to build growing muscles.
Here are some examples.

Draw food that you like to eat that is good for
growing muscles.

**food for
growing
muscles**

What have I learned?

1 I understand that humans have internal skeletons with four functions.

I know this because I can complete the **four** functions of a skeleton in the table.

1.	s_____	**2.**	allow m_____
3.	p_____	**4.**	make b_____ cells

2 I can identify and locate the **skull** and **rib cage**.

I understand their function in protecting important organs.

I know this because I can circle the **skull** and **rib cage** on this skeleton and complete the sentences below.

The skull protects the

_____.

The rib cage protects the

_____ and the

_____.

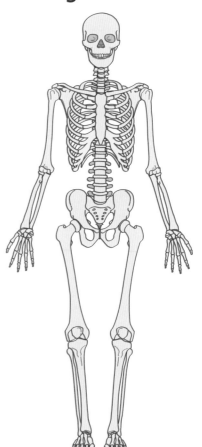

3 I understand the term *joint* as the place where bones meet.
I can describe the range of movement of some different joints.

I know this because I can name:

- one arm joint _____

- one leg joint _____

- a fixed joint _____

- a hinge joint _____

- the joint that moves my arm in a circle _____

4 I understand the terms *contract* and *relax*.
I can describe what pairs of muscles do.
I know this because I can write **contract** or **relax** on **four** labels on these diagrams.

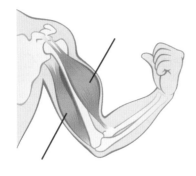 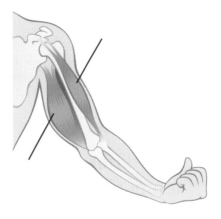

5 I can explain the importance of exercise and diet for healthy muscles and bones.

I know this because I can name one food type that is good for:

- growing muscles _____

- growing bones _____

Solids, liquids and gases

Materials can be solids, liquids or gases. These are states of matter. When a solid is heated it can change state, first to a liquid and then to a gas. When a gas is cooled it can change state, first to a liquid and then to a solid. When water is a solid, we call it ice.

In this topic we will learn:

- how to identify materials as solids, liquids or gases

- how to describe some common properties of solids, liquids and gases

- that solids made of very small particles are a bit like liquids in some ways

- that temperature is a measure of how hot or cold something is

- that temperature is measured in degrees Celsius (°C) using a thermometer

- that water can be in three different states

- that different substances change state at different temperatures.

Does it sometimes get very hot or very cold where you live? When it is hot, puddles of water evaporate quickly. When it is very cold, puddles of water can freeze over.

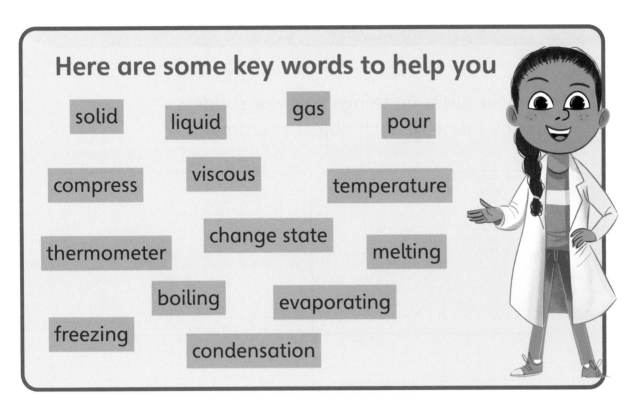

Here are some key words to help you

solid   liquid   gas   pour

compress   viscous   temperature

thermometer   change state   melting

boiling   evaporating

freezing   condensation

Choose two key words from the box above.
Write or draw what they mean.

Solids

1 Draw **four** different things that are **solids**.
Write the name of each object you draw.

2 a) Circle **one** word that means *compress*.

stretch   squash   swing   snap

b) Tick (✔) **all** the statements that correctly describe solids.

Solids can flow.	
Solids keep their shape.	
Solids can be poured.	
Solids are easy to compress.	
Solids have a fixed shape.	

3 This cube is a solid.
Predict what the cube looks like inside each
of these containers.

Draw **one** cube in **each** container for your answer.

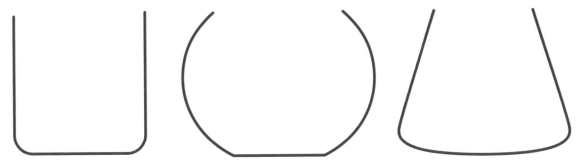

4 Look for **four** solids in **each** picture. Write their names.

Do not choose the same things in each picture.

_____   _____

_____   _____

_____   _____

_____   _____

Liquids

1 a) Draw **three** different liquids in these cups.

b) Now draw the **same** three liquids in these mugs.

c) Explain why the liquids look different shapes in the cups and the mugs.

_____

2 These liquids are in different containers.
Circle all the **beakers**.

3 a) Write **one** word to complete the sentence.

This liquid is being _____.

b) Some of the liquid misses the glass. Explain why that part of the liquid looks like this.

_____

_____

c) Write **one** word to complete the sentence.

This liquid is _____ from one hand to the other.

4 Tick (✔) **all** the statements that correctly describe liquids.

Liquids can flow.	
Liquids change their shape.	
Liquids can be poured.	
Liquids are very easy to compress.	
Liquids take the shape of their container.	

Gases

1. Draw **one** line from each of these to show whether it is is a **solid**, a **liquid** or a **gas**.

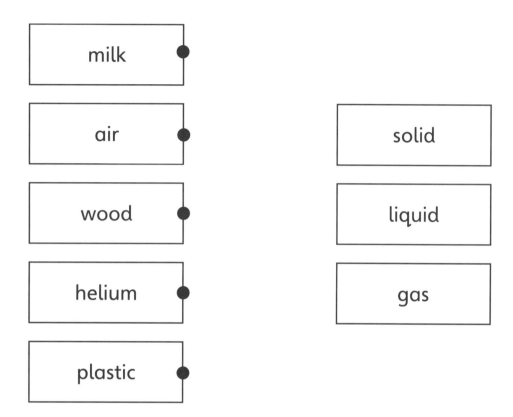

| milk |
| air |
| wood |
| helium |
| plastic |

| solid |
| liquid |
| gas |

2. Tick (✔) **all** the columns next to statements that describe gases.

Gases can be poured.	
Gases change their shape.	
Gases move around.	
Gases are very easy to compress.	
Gases have a fixed shape.	
Gases fill the space they are in.	
Many gases are invisible.	

3 Some balloons stand up very straight like this.

a) Which gas is inside this balloon? _____

b) Which gas is all around us? _____

4 A scientist has brown gas in a jar.

What happens if she takes the lid off?

Draw your prediction in the box below.

lid —

5 a) Maria blows some bubbles.
Circle the bubble that has the **most** gas inside it.

b) Name the gas that is inside
the bubbles.

_____

Solid, liquid or gas?

① a) Label this drink to show a **solid**, a **liquid** and a **gas**.
Use a word and a label line each time.

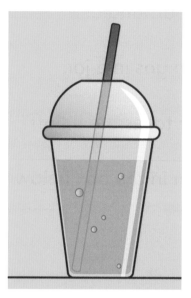

b) Rio blows lots of air down the straw.
Draw on the picture what the drink looks now.

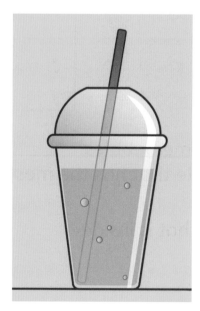

② Name **two** different gases.

1. _____ 2. _____

3 a) Look at these two pictures.

juice

sand

Complete the sentences using words from the box.
Words can be used only **once**.

| liquid | gas | solid | pile |
| pool | grain | tiny | big |

Juice is a _____ and sand is a _____.

When it is not in a container, juice makes a

_____, but sand makes a _____.

Sand is made of lots of grains. Each _____ is

a _____ solid.

b) Which **two** of these have properties most like **sand**?
Circle **two** words.

oranges   sugar   wood   metal   salt   milk

Comparing liquids

1. The picture shows some honey.

   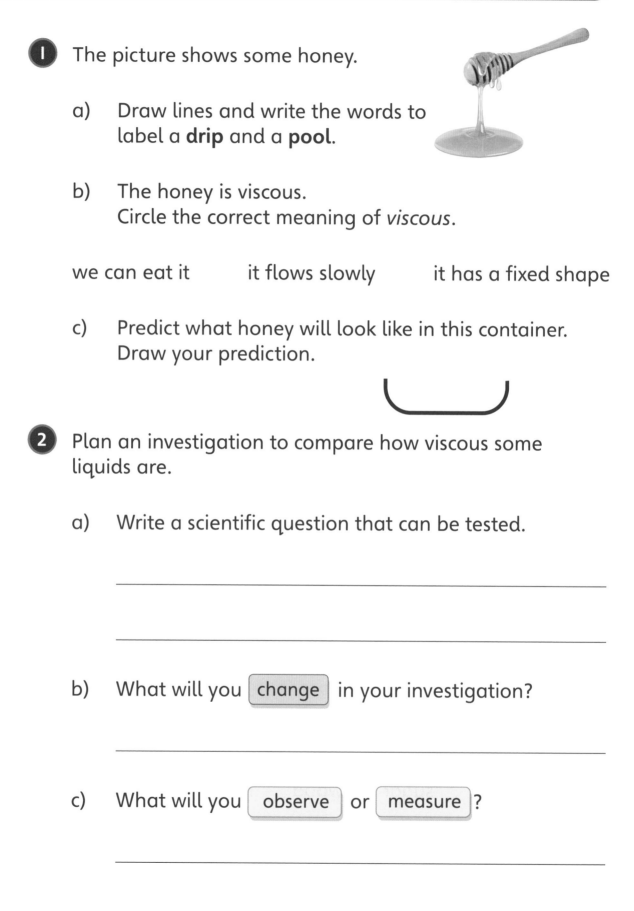

   a) Draw lines and write the words to label a **drip** and a **pool**.

   b) The honey is viscous.
      Circle the correct meaning of *viscous*.

   we can eat it   it flows slowly   it has a fixed shape

   c) Predict what honey will look like in this container.
      Draw your prediction.

2. Plan an investigation to compare how viscous some liquids are.

   a) Write a scientific question that can be tested.

   _____

   _____

   b) What will you [change] in your investigation?

   _____

   c) What will you [observe] or [measure]?

   _____

d)   Predict which liquid is most viscous.   _____

e)   Draw and label your equipment.

3   a)   Complete the table for your results.

- Put the names of the liquids in the **first** column.

- Put units for time in the column heading **only**.

b)   Write a conclusion to answer your scientific question.

_____

_____

Temperature

1 Write **hot** or **cold** under each picture.

2 This learner is measuring.

a) Circle **one** word to show what she is measuring.

colour   length   temperature   time

b) Name the measuring equipment she is using.

_____

3 This child is eating food.

a) Do you think the food is **hot** or **cold**?

_____

b) What evidence is there to support your choice?

_____

c)   Draw a picture of a place that is **hot** and a place that is **cold**.

hot

cold

Using a thermometer

1 a) What is a thermometer used to measure?
Write **one** word.

_____

b) In what unit is temperature measured?

Write it in **words** on the line.   Write the **symbol** in the box.

unit _____

2 a) Complete the scale on this thermometer by writing the missing numbers.

b) What temperature does the thermometer show? Write the unit too.

_____

c) Colour in more of the red part to show 21°C.

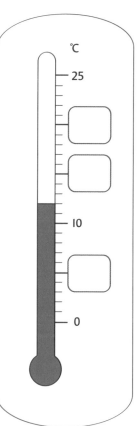

3 What is this sort of thermometer used for?

_____

4 a) Complete the **scale** on this thermometer by writing the missing numbers.

b) What temperature does the thermometer show?

_____

c) Colour in more of the red part to show 32 °C.

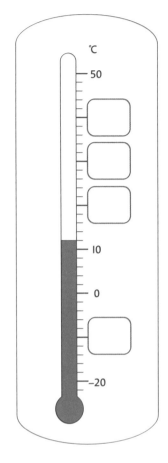

5 Write the temperature each thermometer scale shows.
Hint: write the missing numbers on the scales first.

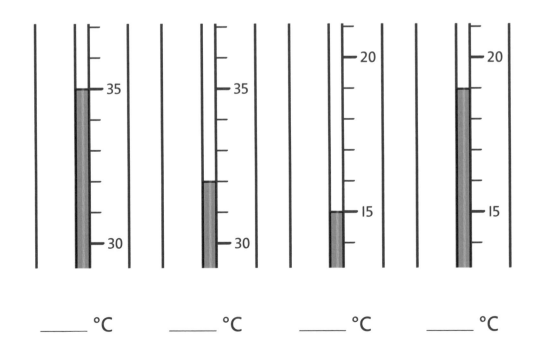

_____ °C   _____ °C   _____ °C   _____ °C

Changing state

1 a) What is happening to this ice cream? Write **one** word.

_____

b) Use a word and a line to label a part that is **solid** and a part that is **liquid**.

c) Solid and liquid are two states of matter.

Name **one** other state of matter. _____

2 Gold is a metal.
The picture shows hot, liquid gold.

a) Describe **one** thing you can see happening that shows this gold is a liquid.

_____

b) What state will the gold change into when it is cooled?

_____

3 Kasim says that this cheese, tomato and olive pizza is hot.

What evidence can you see to support his suggestion?

_____

4 The pictures show similar size blocks of gold, chocolate and butter.

| **gold** | **chocolate** | **butter** |

Predict which one needs the highest temperature

to make it melt. _____

5 The graph shows the temperature at which three different materials (**A**, **B** and **C**) melt.

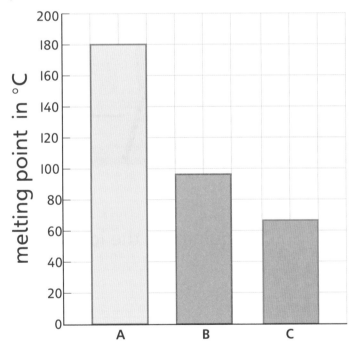

a) At what temperature does **A** melt? _____

b) Which material melts at the lowest temperature? _____

c) Are any of them liquids at 100 °C? If so, which?

_____

States of water

1 Water can be in three different states.
Write the name of **one** state under **each** picture.

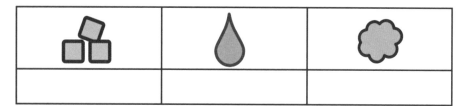

2 The diagram shows some ice cubes being heated.

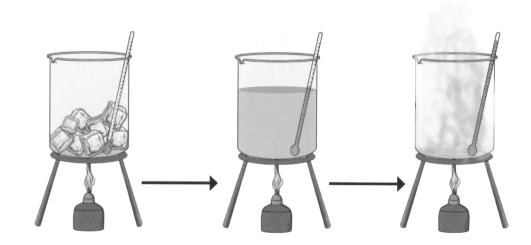

a) Name the glass equipment the ice cubes are in.

_____

b) (i) Write **liquid**, **solid** or **gas** *under* each part of the diagram.

   (ii) Write **water**, **water vapour** or **ice** *above* each part of the diagram.

   (iii) Write **evaporating** or **melting** on the two *arrows*.

3 Sudhir has a beaker of hot water. He measures the temperature of the water regularly and plots this graph.

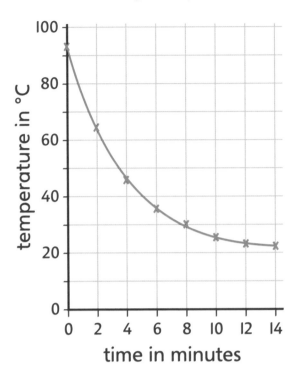

a) Name **two** pieces of measuring equipment he needs.

1. _____ 2. _____

b) How many times does Sudhir measure the temperature of the water? ⬭

c) How long does he wait before taking the next measurement? _____

d) Circle the result on the graph that shows when the water is at 30 °C.

e) Sudhir says the water is cooling. What evidence can you see on the graph that supports his statement?

_____

More about water

1　The diagram shows water changing state.

a)　Write **gas**, **liquid** or **solid** beside each picture.
Write them all on the same side.

b)　On the other side of each picture, write **water**, **ice** or **water vapour**.

c)　Write **one** word from the box beside each of the red and blue arrows.

| melting | condensation | freezing | evaporation |

2 Complete the sentences to describe the pictures.

On a cold window, water vapour in the

_____ changes to liquid water.

This is called _____.

Liquid water on this tap has changed to a

_____ called ice.

This is called _____.

3 Look at the thermometer on page 91 of your Textbook.

a) At what temperature does water **boil**? _____

b) At what temperature does water **freeze**? _____

c) In which state is water at **60 °C**? _____

d) In which state is water at **120 °C**? _____

4 A learner says this can must be very cold.

What evidence can you see that supports
their statement?

_____

_____

What have I learned?

1 I can identify materials as solids, liquids or gases and I can see which they are.

I know this because I can write **solid**, **liquid** or **gas** under these pictures.

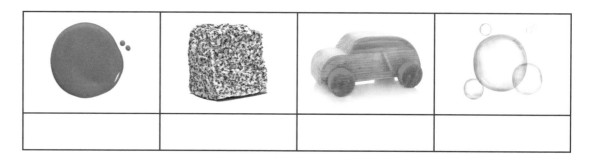

2 I can describe some common properties of solids, liquids and gases.

I know this because I can write **one** property of each.

solid: _____

liquid: _____

gas: _____

3 I understand that solids made of very small particles are a bit like liquids in some ways.

I know this because I can describe a property of solid sand that makes it look a bit like a liquid.

_____

4 I understand that temperature is a measure of how hot or cold something is.

I understand that temperature is measured in degrees Celsius (°C) using a thermometer.

I know this because I can write the temperature shown on this thermometer.

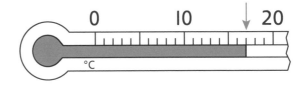

_____

5 I understand that water can be in three different states and changes from one state to another at different temperatures.

I know this because I know that water boils at _____ °C

and freezes at _____ °C.

6 I understand that different substances change state at different temperatures.

I know this because I know that ice melts at a

_____ temperature than metal.

Making and changing sounds

Sounds come from a source. Sounds travel through solids, liquids and gases as vibrations. We can change the volume of sounds to make them louder or quieter.

In this topic we will learn:

- that sounds come from a source and can travel through solids, liquids and gases

- that vibrations from sounds travel through a medium to the ear

- that some materials can prevent vibrations from a sound source reaching the ear

- that volume means how loud a sound is and that the volume of a sound can be changed

- that there are high- and low-pitched sounds and that the pitch of a sound can be changed

- to find patterns between the pitch of a sound and the features of the object that made it.

Have you ever heard a gull like me make a sound? I make a loud squawk when I'm looking for food. Can you change your voice to make a very deep sound or a very quiet sound?

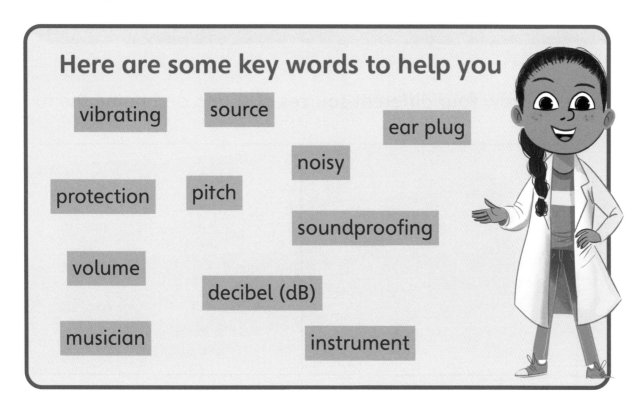

Here are some key words to help you

vibrating   source   ear plug

noisy

protection   pitch

soundproofing

volume

decibel (dB)

musician   instrument

Choose two key words from the box above.
Write or draw what they mean.

Vibrations

1 a) Draw **four** different sources of sound and name them.

b) Think of **four** different ways you can make sounds with your voice.

1. _____ 2. _____

3. _____ 4. _____

c)   (i)   Which sense organ do you use to listen to sounds?

_____

(ii)   What is this sense called? _____

2 a)   Try doing this with a plastic ruler, then draw arrows on the diagram to show how the ruler moves.

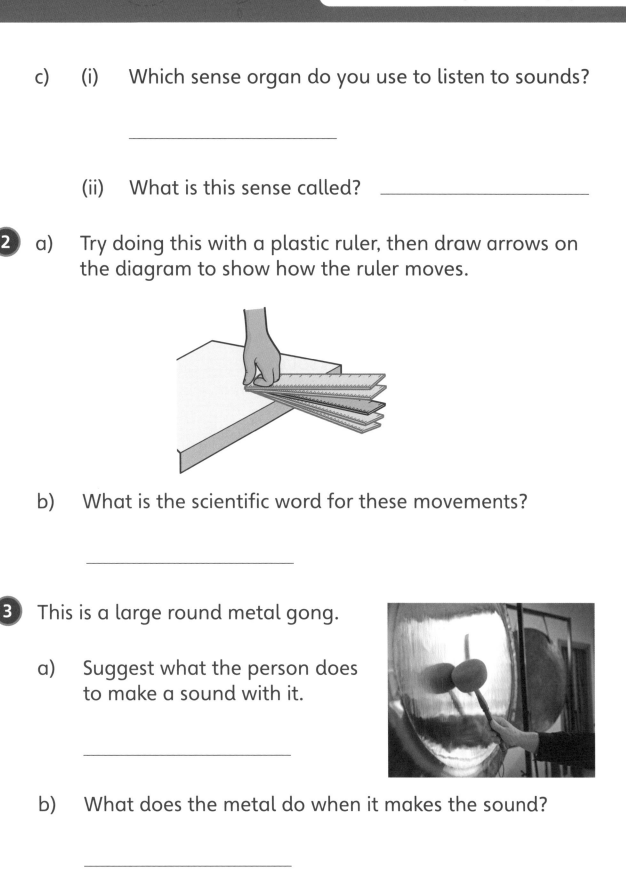

b)   What is the scientific word for these movements?

_____

3 This is a large round metal gong.

a)   Suggest what the person does to make a sound with it.

_____

b)   What does the metal do when it makes the sound?

_____

c)   Name **one** other musical instrument that makes a

sound in a similar way. _____

Travelling sound

1 Complete the sentences by writing **one** word in each space.

Sounds come from a _____ of sound.

We hear sounds with our _____.

Sounds travel as _____.

Sound can travel through solids, _____

and _____.

2 a) Name the gas that is all around us. _____

b) Is water a solid, a liquid or a gas? _____

c) Is wood a solid, a liquid or a gas? _____

d) Which state of matter does sound travel through

fastest? _____

3 Can sounds travel in space? _____

Give a reason for your answer.

_____

4 These learners are investigating sound.

a) Describe what they are doing.

_____

b) Try the investigation with a partner. What happens?

_____

5 Two learners ask, 'Can sound travel through water?'
They have:

- **a bucket of water**
- **a big plastic bottle**
- **two metal spoons**.

Draw or write how they could use this equipment to answer their question.

Soundproofing

1 **a)** Draw a picture of **two** different things that make a very loud sound. Write what they are below each picture.

```
┌─────────────────┐  ┌─────────────────┐
│                 │  │                 │
│                 │  │                 │
│                 │  │                 │
│                 │  │                 │
│                 │  │                 │
├─────────────────┤  ├─────────────────┤
│                 │  │                 │
└─────────────────┘  └─────────────────┘
```

b) Write the missing word to finish the sentence.

Objects that make sounds are sound _____.

c) Listen to sounds around you. Now put your hands over your ears.

(i) What happens to the sound?

_____

(ii) Explain why this happens. Use the word **vibrations** in your answer.

_____

_____

2 There may be loud noises at the place where this person works.

a) Write **one** piece of evidence from the picture that supports this statement.

_____

b) Circle **one** piece of safety equipment below that protects people from loud noise.

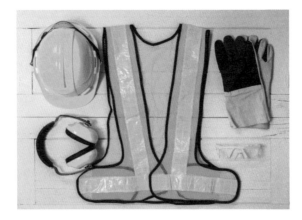

3 The walls of this room have soundproofing material stuck to them.

Explain what *soundproof* means.

_____

_____

Investigating soundproofing

Plan an investigation to find out about soundproofing.

1 Write a scientific question for your investigation.

_____

2 What will you [change] in your investigation?

_____

3 a) What will you use as the source of sound?

_____

b) What will you [observe] or [measure]?

_____

c) How will you do this?

_____

_____

4 Write **two** things that you will keep the same in the investigation.

I. _____

2. _____

5 Draw **four** materials that you could use to test soundproofing. Add labels to your drawing.

6 Do your investigation. Complete this results table.

Material	Score out of 10
No material	

Use your results to answer your scientific question.

_____

_____

7 Suggest **one** way you could improve your investigation.

_____

_____

Volume of sounds

1 a)   Write **loud** or **quiet** *above* each picture.

b)   Draw an animal that makes loud sounds and an
     animal that makes quiet sounds *below* each picture.

2 Complete the sentence.

The loudness of a sound depends on how big the

_____ are.

3 Put some rice on a drum skin.

a)   Tap the drum gently.
     Describe what happens to the rice.

_____

b)   Tap the drum harder. Describe what happens.

_____

4 Link these pairs of statements into one sentence.
Use two words ending in -er each time.

| how hard you tap the drum | and | the size of the vibrations |

_____

| how hard you tap the drum | and | the loudness of the sound |

_____

| how hard you tap the drum | and | how high the rice moves |

_____

| the size of the vibrations | and | the volume of the sound |

_____

Measuring the volume of sounds

1 Circle the place where the volume is **loudest** on pictures **A**, **B** and **C**.

A

B

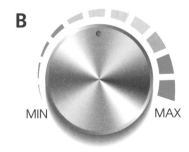

MIN   MAX

C

2 a) How do loud sounds affect our hearing?

_____

b) Write the scientific word for the loudness of a sound.

_____

3 a) In what unit is the loudness of a sound measured?

Write the **word** on the line.
Write the **symbol** in the box.

unit _____

b) Name **two** pieces of equipment that can be used to measure the loudness of a sound.

1. _____   2. _____

4 a) Name **two** different machines that can be operated with a remote control.

1. _____

2. _____

b) A remote control can switch a sound off.

Write **one** other thing that a remote control can do to a sound.

_____

5 Grace can play four different musical instruments.

For each instrument, describe how to make the volume louder.

Measuring in decibels (dB)

1. Draw a place where you go that has:

   - **loud** background noise

   - **quiet** background noise.

   Name the places you draw under the pictures.

Loud background noise	Quiet background noise

2. Look at this information.

faint sound	very loud sound	extremely loud sound

   30 dB   40 dB   50 dB   60 dB   70 dB   80 dB   90 dB   100 dB   110 dB   120 dB   130 dB   140 dB

   a) Describe a sound that is between 80 and 90 dB.

   _____

   b) Describe a sound that is below 50 dB.

   _____

3 Answer the questions using the decibel scale on page 109 of your textbook.

a) How loud is a hairdryer?

_____ dB

b) What makes a sound of 40 dB?

_____

c) What makes the loudest sound shown?

_____

d) Which is louder, a truck or a trombone?

_____

e) Name **two** sounds that are louder than a police siren.

1. _____ 2. _____

f) Why are there no words or picture at 0 dB?

_____

Pitch

1 a) What do scientists call something that makes sounds?

_____

b) What do our ears allow us to do? _____

c) How do sounds travel from the place that makes them to the place we hear them?

_____

2 a) When we are talking about sounds, what does the word *pitch* mean?

_____

b) (i) Circle the **two** animals that make the lowest-pitched sounds.

(ii) The **size** of an animal often affects the pitch of the sounds it can make. Complete the sentence.

The _____ the animal, the lower the pitch of the sound it can make.

3 Investigate the sound that different lengths of a plastic ruler make.

a) Write a scientific question for your investigation.

_____

b) What are you [changing]?

_____

c) (i) What does the ruler do when you pull it down and let go? _____

(ii) Why do you need to pull the ruler down with the same force each time?

_____

d) How does the pitch of the sound change as you make the moving part shorter?

_____

e) Complete the sentences using words that end in -er.

(i) The _____ the length of the vibrating part, the slower it vibrates. We hear a lower sound.

(ii) The shorter the length of the vibrating part, the

_____ it vibrates. We hear a

_____ sound.

Investigating pitch

1 Write **one** scientific word for **each** description.

How loud or quiet a sound is _____

How high or low a sound is _____

2 This musical instrument can make sounds.

a) What is the scientific word for something that can make sounds?

_____

b) How could you make sounds with this instrument?

_____

c) What would you do to make the sounds louder?

_____

d) (i) Write **high** or **low** under each end of the instrument to show how the sounds it makes differ.

(ii) Complete the sentence using a word ending in -er.

The _____ the metal bar, the lower the pitch of the sound it makes.

3 Make this musical instrument using glass bottles containing different volumes of water.

a) Name the equipment used to measure the volume of water to go into each bottle.

   _____

b) Write **two** things that you must keep the same when you make and play this instrument.

   1. _____

   2. _____

c) There are two ways to make sounds with the bottles.

   (i) Which way makes the **air** in the bottle vibrate?

   _____

   (ii) Which way makes the **water** vibrate?

   _____

d) Tap each bottle and listen to the sound. Describe how it changes by finishing this sentence.

   The more water in the bottle, the _____ the pitch of the sound.

Other ways to change pitch

1 Design **two** string instruments that you could make.

a) Draw your designs here. Label the parts.

Design 1

Design 2

b)   For each of your designs, describe how to:

- make the sounds louder or quieter

- make high or low sounds.

Design 1

Louder/quieter: _____

_____

High/low: _____

_____

Design 2

Louder/quieter: _____

_____

High/low: _____

_____

2 a)   What is meant by the **volume** of a sound?

_____

b)   What is the scientific word for **how high or low** a sound is?

_____

Strings and drums

1　a)　Which letter shows a vibrating string?　_____

A
B
C
D
E

b)　Which letter shows the thinnest string?　_____

c)　Which string makes a sound with the highest pitch? _____

d)　How do sounds from musical instruments reach our ears?

_____

e)　Complete the sentences about vibrating strings using words from the box.

faster　slower　higher　lower　louder　quieter

The thicker the string, the _____ it vibrates.

The thicker the string, the _____ the pitch.

The harder the string is plucked, the _____ the volume of the sound.

2 a)   Which instrument has the longest strings?   _____

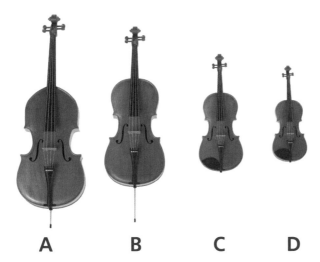

A   **B**   **C**   **D**

b)   Which instrument makes sounds with the highest pitch?

_____

c)   Write **one** missing word.

The shorter the string, the _____ the pitch.

3   The pictures show two instruments being tuned.

a)   When the drum skin is tighter does it
vibrate faster or slower?

_____

b)   When the violin string is tighter does it
make a higher or lower sound?

_____

c)   Write **one** missing word.

The tighter the skin or string, the _____
the pitch of the musical note.

Wind instruments

1 Write **wood** or **metal** under each instrument to show what they are made from.

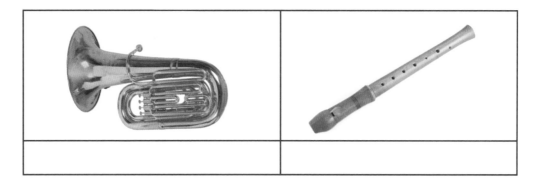

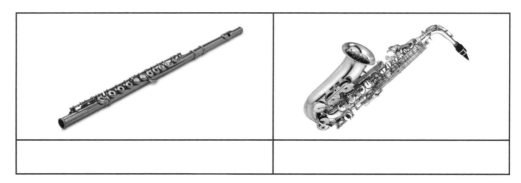

2 a)   Circle the clarinet with the shortest tube.

A B C   D

b)   Which clarinet has the longest column of air in it?   _____

c)   Describe how the length of the tube affects the pitch of sound.

Hint: remember to use -er words.

lower-pitched sounds

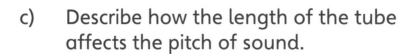

_____

_____

3 a) (i) Predict which instrument makes the lowest-pitched sounds.

⬜

(ii) Why did you choose this instrument?

_____

b) (i) Predict which **two** instruments play notes of similar pitch.

⬜ and ⬜

(ii) Why did you choose these two instruments?

_____

4 a) Name this instrument.

_____

b) How does this instrument make sounds?

_____

c) Describe how a musician plays notes with lower or higher pitch.

_____

_____

What have I learned?

1 I can explain that sounds come from a source and can travel through solids, liquids and gases.

I understand that vibrations from sounds travel through a medium to the ear.

I know this because I can describe how we hear a

phone ringing. _____

_____

2 I understand that some materials can prevent vibrations from a sound source reaching the ear.

I know this because I can write the name of **one**

soundproofing material. _____

3 I understand that volume means how loud a sound is and this volume can be changed.

I know it is possible to measure the volume of sounds in decibels (dB).

I know this because I can name this equipment.

_____

I can also circle the loudest sound from this list.

whisper   shout   firework   car

4 I can find patterns between the volume of a sound and the strength of the vibrations that made it.

I know this because I can complete this sentence.

The bigger the vibrations, the _____ the volume.

5 I know that there are high- and low-pitched sounds and that the pitch of a sound can be changed.

I know this because I can write **high** and **low** beside the pipes of this instrument.

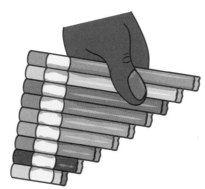

6 I can find patterns between the pitch of a sound and the features of the object that made it.

I can identify and describe these features, such as the length of the tube, the length of the string and how tight the string is.

I know this because I can complete these sentences.

The longer the tube, the _____ the pitch.

The longer the string, the _____ the pitch.

The tighter the string, the _____ the pitch.

Electricity: everyday uses and simple circuits

We use electricity at school and at home. Electrical appliances keep our food cool, boil our water and wash our clothes. When it is dark, we can switch lights on to help us see things. Smartphones, smartwatches and tablets need their batteries charged with electricity.

In this topic we will learn:

- about some uses of electricity and how to identify appliances that use mains electricity or batteries

- about the dangers of mains electricity

- how to make simple circuits and that only complete circuits will work

- the names of components in a circuit and how to identify them

- that some materials conduct electricity better than others

- about the use of electrical conductors and insulators.

Humans use electricity to keep food cool, to wash clothes and to light their houses.

Can you think of things in your home that need electricity or batteries to work?

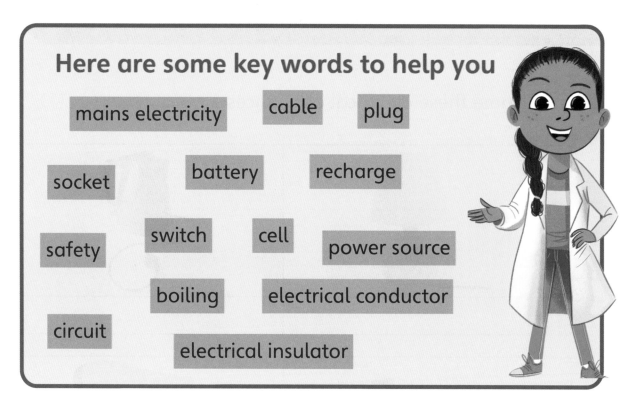

Here are some key words to help you

mains electricity   cable   plug

socket   battery   recharge

safety   switch   cell   power source

boiling   electrical conductor

circuit   electrical insulator

Choose two key words from the box above.
Write or draw what they mean.

Electricity

1 a) Name these electrical appliances.

b) Circle the **cable** on each picture.

c) You can see a plug on some of the cables.
Plugs differ around the world.

Draw what a **plug** looks like where you live.

d) What are plugs plugged into on a wall?

Write **one** word. _____

2 a) Name these electrical appliances.

b) Draw **two** different electrical appliances you have at home or at school that only plug in to mains electricity.

Batteries

1   a)   Name these devices that use batteries that have to be changed.

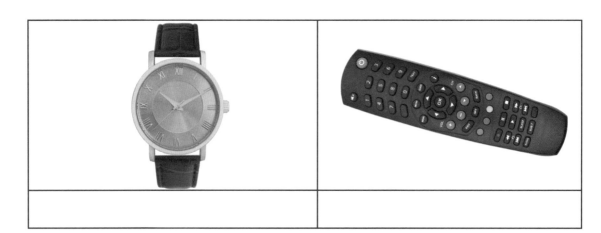

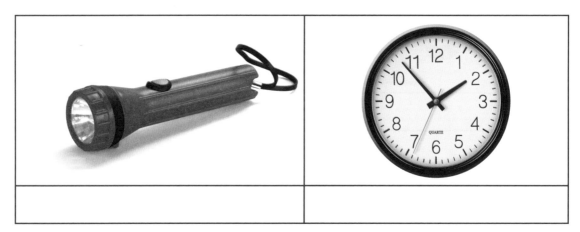

b)   Draw **two** objects that you have seen with batteries that have to be changed.

2 a) Circle the symbol that shows a device with a rechargeable battery that will stop working soon.

b) Smartphones have rechargeable batteries.

Describe what is happening in the picture.

_____

_____

c) Draw **two** devices that you have seen with rechargeable batteries.
Write their names too.

Electrical safety

1 Write some rules for staying safe with mains electricity. Use the pictures to help you.

_____

_____

_____

_____

_____

_____

_____

_____

_____

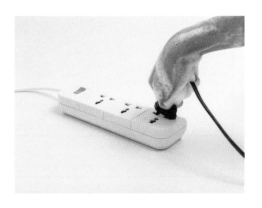

_____

_____

_____

_____

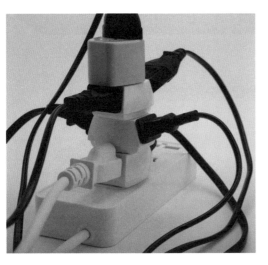

_____

_____

_____

_____

_____

_____

_____

_____

_____

_____

2 Make a poster warning people that mains electricity is dangerous. Here are some ideas and words to start with.

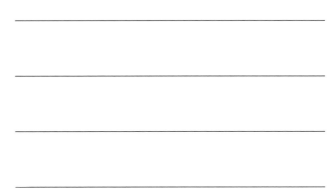

Electrical components

1 a) Name this electrical component.

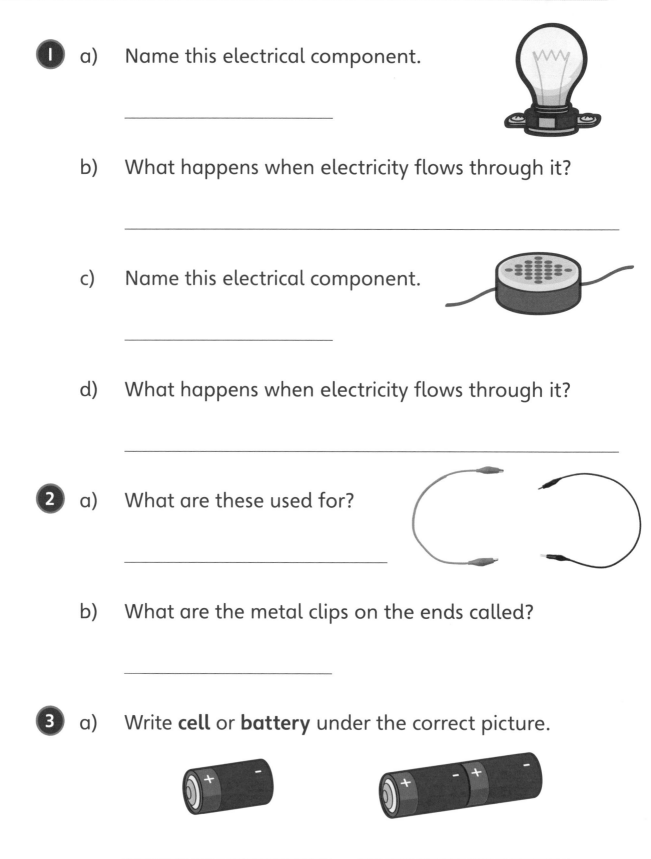

_____

b) What happens when electricity flows through it?

_____

c) Name this electrical component.

_____

d) What happens when electricity flows through it?

_____

2 a) What are these used for?

_____

b) What are the metal clips on the ends called?

_____

3 a) Write **cell** or **battery** under the correct picture.

_____   _____

b) Explain the difference between the terms *cell* and *battery*.

_____

_____

c) What is the function of a cell in a circuit?

_____

_____

4 A learner makes this.

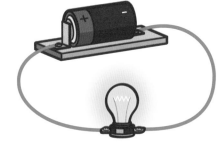

a) What has the learner made?

_____

b) What flows in the wires? _____

c) Write **one** piece of evidence that shows the equipment is working.

_____

5 A learner wants to put two cells in here.

Draw **two** cells in the space below to show the correct way round to put them in. Write **+** and **−** on the cells.

Complete circuits

1 a) Name **this component**.

_____

b) Write **open** or **closed** under each picture.

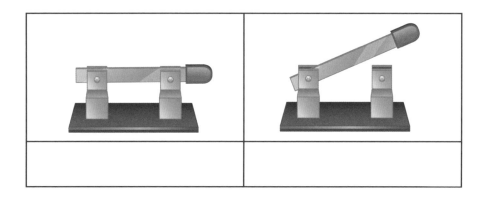

c) Complete the sentences.

When **this component** is **open** it _____ the circuit.

When **this component** is **closed** it _____ the circuit.

2 a) Draw a line from each word to label this circuit.

cell

wire

bulb

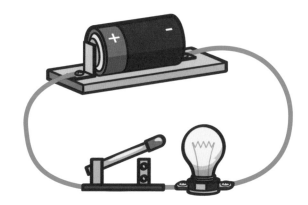

b) Suggest **one** reason why the bulb in part (a) is not lit.

_____

3 This bulb lights, but it soon stops working.

Suggest **one** thing you could do to try to make the bulb light again.

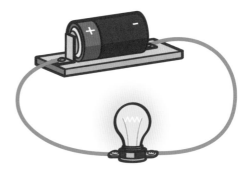

_____

4 The diagrams show **circuit 1** and **circuit 2**.

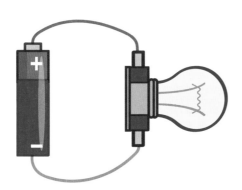   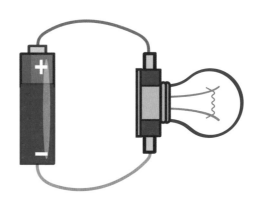

circuit 1   circuit 2

Explain why the bulb is lit in **circuit 1** but not lit in **circuit 2**.

_____

_____

_____

_____

Investigating circuits

1 Make this circuit if you can. If not, predict the results.

    a) Write a list of the equipment you need.

_____

    b) Join the components together.

        (i) What must you do to make the bulbs light?

_____

        (ii) Circle the best description of your lit bulbs.

          very bright   bright   dim

2 Now make this change to your circuit.

    a) Describe the change you are making.

_____

    b) What is the function of the component you are changing?

_____

    c) Circle the best description of your lit bulbs now.

        very bright   bright   dim

3 a) Make this circuit. Do the bulbs light? _____

b) Move the switch to **A**. Do the
bulbs light? _____

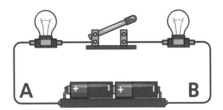

c) Move the switch to **B**. Do the bulbs light? _____

d) Write a conclusion about the position of the switch.

_____

e) Put **two** switches in the circuit. Do you need to close
both switches to make the bulbs light?

_____

4 Write **one** word to complete the sentences below the
pictures.

a)

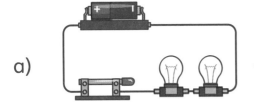 and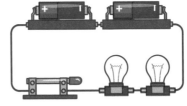

More cells in the circuit makes both bulbs _____.

b)

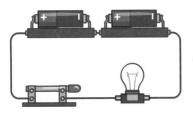 and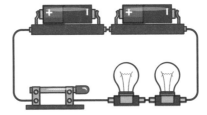

More bulbs in the circuit makes each bulb _____.

Using circuits to make things

Design **two** different things that light up, buzz or move using a circuit.

1 a) List the equipment you need for your first design.

_____

_____

_____

b) Draw your circuit.

c) Draw your finished object. Write how it works.

2 a) List the equipment you need for your second design.

_____

_____

_____

b) Draw your circuit.

c) Draw your finished object. Write how it works.

Electrical conductors

1. Test some materials to see if they are electrical conductors.

   a) Complete the drawing of the circuit you use.

   b) What are you [changing] in this investigation?

   _____

   c) Why is a bulb needed in the circuit?

   _____

2. a) What does the term *electrical conductor* mean?

   _____

   b) Find objects made from different materials.

   Predict which materials will be good electrical conductors.

   _____

   _____

   _____

3 Test the materials and write your results in the table.

Object	Material it is made from	Score out of 10

a) Which materials are good conductors?

_____

b) Which materials did not conduct electricity?

_____

4 a) Describe **one** problem with observing brightness and scoring it out of 10.

_____

_____

b) Suggest **one** way you could improve this or any other part of the investigation.

_____

_____

Conductors and insulators

1 a) Name the material each ball is made of.

b) These materials are electrical insulators.
What does *electrical insulator* mean?

_____

2 Metals are good electrical conductors.

a) What does *electrical conductor* mean?

_____

b) Name **two** metals that are very good electrical conductors.

I. _____ 2. _____

3 These are plugs from electrical appliances.

a) Which plug is most like plugs

where you live? _____

A

B

C

b) Use label lines and the words to label these plugs.

(i) Label **plastic** and **metal** on this plug.

(ii) Label **good conductor** and **good insulator** on this plug.

c) Why is most of the plug made of plastic?

_____

4 The picture shows a wall socket and its switch.

Predict, by ticking (✔) **one** box, whether they are:

good conductors   or   **good insulators**

☐   ☐

Give a reason for your choice.

_____

_____

Conductors and insulators at home

1 Use label lines and the words in **bold** to label these electrical cables.

a) Label **plastic** and **copper** on this cable.

b) Label **good conductor** and **good insulator** on this cable.

c) Explain how plastic makes this cable safer to use.

_____

_____

2 a) Label **one** place you can see copper in this cable.

b)   What may happen if someone touches this cable?

_____

_____

3 The picture shows an electrical cable on fire.

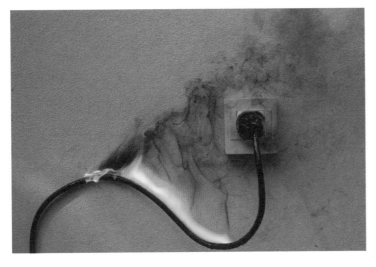

a)   Circle the place you think the fire started.

b)   Suggest why this happened.

Use the words **touch** and **overheat** in your answer.

_____

_____

_____

_____

What have I learned?

1 I understand some uses of electricity and can identify appliances that use mains electricity and that use batteries.

I know this because I can name **two** appliances that **only** use mains electricity and **two** that use batteries.

Mains: _____ and _____

Batteries: _____ and _____

2 I can describe the dangers of mains electricity.

I know this because I can describe what is dangerous in each picture.

_____

_____

_____

_____

3 I can make simple circuits and I know that only complete circuits will work.

I can do this by following instructions or looking at pictures.

I know this because I can show a working circuit I have made to a partner or my teacher.

4 I can identify and name components in a circuit and understand that a switch can be used to break a circuit.

I know this because I can name these components.

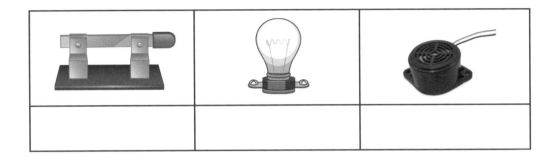

5 I understand that a circuit needs a power source to work.

I know this because I can circle the circuit that does **not** have a power source.

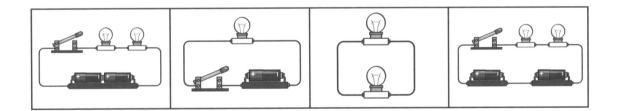

6 I understand that some materials conduct electricity better than others.

I understand the use of electrical *conductors* and *insulators* and I can use these words correctly.

I know this because I can label **conductor** and **insulator** on this diagram. I can also name the materials.

These materials are _____ and _____.

My notes

My notes

My notes

My notes